The Joy of Classics

The Joy Of Classics contains original piano compositions by the masters in the easy-to-intermediate grades. The word "classics" in our title designates a somewhat broader category than the Haydn, Mozart, Beethoven period. That is, it indicates "works which have held their place as masterpieces in general estimation for considerable time..."* In this sense the word "classic" is contrasted with the word "modern." In other words, The Joy Of Classics contains time-honored, shorter piano works of the 18th and 19th centuries, from Scarlatti and Purcell to Brahms and Tchaikowsky.

In addition to a number of well known miniatures, the player will find some pieces which are published here for the first time in the United States.

All pieces are in their original form   Expression marks were added and in some cases minor editorial adjustments were made to clarify and facilitate the understanding of the piece.

The entire contents of The Joy Of Classics is "living" music, brimming with melodic, rhythmic and emotional interest. It affords an entertaining and instructive musical experience from the first page to the last.

*Grove's Dictionary.

78 6-4 JOY

Distributed throughout the world by:
Music Sales
257 Park Avenue South, New York, NY 10010, USA.

8/9 Frith Street, London W1V 5TZ, England.

120 Rothschild Avenue, Rosebery, NSW2018, Australia.

Contents

Composer's Index

Air

John Blow
(1649-1708)

Andantino

Gavotte

Arcangelo Corelli
(1653 – 1713)

The Queen's Dolour

Henry Purcell
(1658–1695)

Rigadoon

Andante con moto

Henry Purcell
(1658 - 1695)

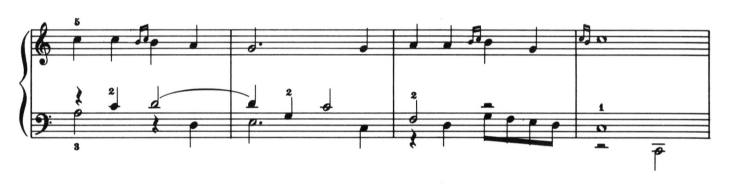

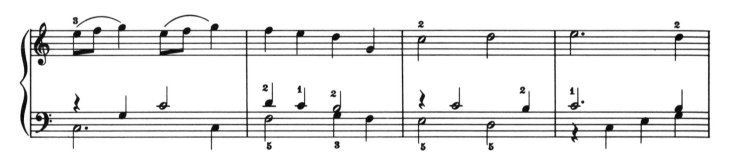

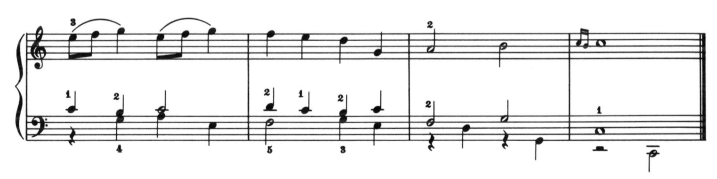

Pastorale

Con moto; alla siciliana

Domenico Zipoli
(1688 – 1726)

Allegro

Domenico Scarlatti
(1685–1757)

Sonata
Minuet

Domenico Scarlatti
(1685 – 1757)

Andantino

Little Prelude ✓

Johann Sebastian Bach
(1685 – 1750)

Allegro moderato

Aria

from the Anna Magdalena Bach Notebook

Johann Sebastian Bach
(1685 - 1750)

Invention

Georg Friedrich Händel
(1685 – 1759)

Dance Song

Sperontes (J. S. Scholze)
(1705 – 1750)

Andantino

Gavotte and Musette

from English Suite No. 3

Johann Sebastian Bach
(1685 – 1750)

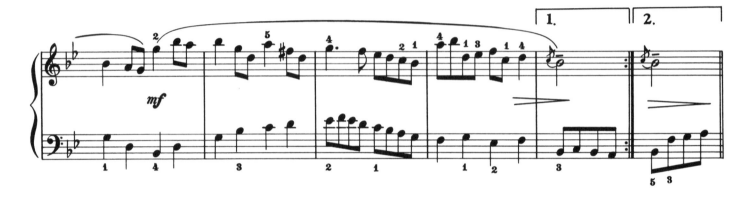

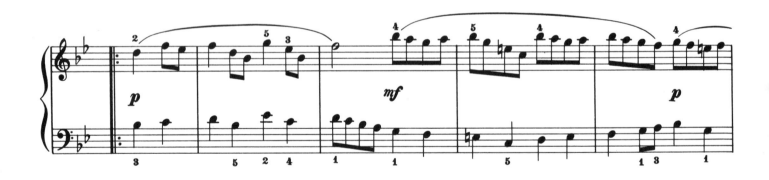

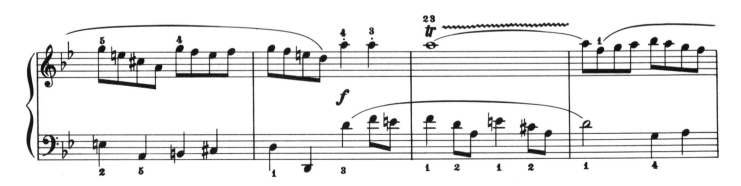

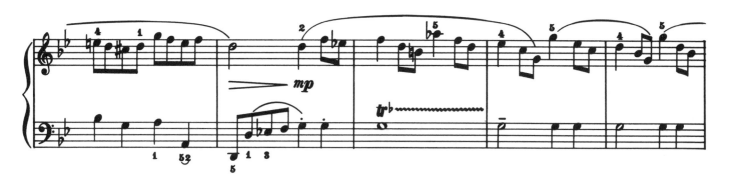

(Segue Musette)

Musette

Johann Sebastian Bach
(1685 - 1750)

Andante pastorale

Gavotte D.C. al Fine

Musical Pastime

Valentin Rathgeber
(1682 – 1750)

Aylesford Piece

Georg Friedrich Händel
(1685 – 1759)

Vivace

Arioso

Georg Philipp Telemann
(1681 – 1767)

(Segue Burlesca)

Burlesca

Georg Philipp Telemann

L'épineuse*

The Thorny One

François Couperin
(1668 – 1733)

D.C. al Fine

* Theme and First Couplet

Les Moissonneurs*

The Harvesters

François Couperin

Giocoso

* *Theme and First Couplet*

Noël

Louis-Claude Daquin
(1694 – 1772)

Allegretto

Air en Gavotte

Christoph Graupner
(1683 – 1760)

Tambourin

Jean Philippe Rameau
(1683–1764)

*Play all ornaments on the beat

La Xenophon

Carl Philipp Emanuel Bach
(1714 – 1788)

* *Original Key C♯*

Scherzino

Georg Philipp Telemann
(1681 – 1767)

Vivace

Carillons

Johann Philipp Kirnberger
(1721 – 1783)

Andante

from Toccata in G minor

João de Sousa Carvalho
(1745 – 1798)

Anglaise

Karl von Dittersdorf
(1739 – 1799)

Allegretto

Schwaebisch
Austrian Peasant Dance

Johann Philipp Kirnberger
(1721 – 1783)

Bourrée

Johann Ludwig Krebs
(1713 – 1780)

Allegretto

Allegretto Grazioso

Johann Christian Bach
(1735 - 1782)

Minuet

Carl Philipp Emanuel Bach
(1714 – 1788)

Andante mesto

Little Serenade
German Dance

Joseph Haydn
(1732 – 1809)

Minuet

from Piano Sonata No. 3

Joseph Haydn
(1732 - 1809)

Con moto grazioso

Trio

D.C. al Fine

Sonatina

Daniel Gottlob Türk
(1756–1813)

(segue Finale)

Finale
Allegro

Repeat Finale till sign (⊕),
then play Coda.

⊕ **Coda**

Arietta

Wolfgang Amadeus Mozart
(1756 – 1791)

Contredance

Wolfgang Amadeus Mozart
(1756 – 1791)

Allegro

Gypsy Dance

Joseph Haydn
(1732–1809)

Trio

Allegro

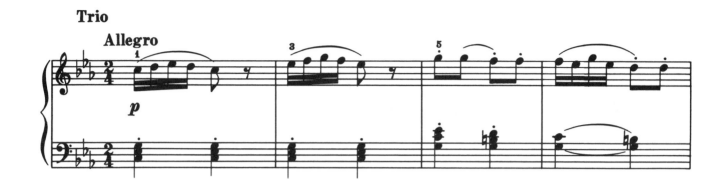

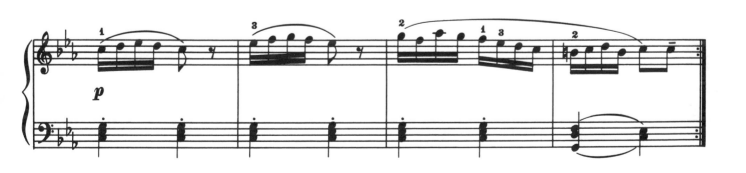

Polonaise

Wolfgang Amadeus Mozart
(1756 – 1791)

Spring Song

"Come, Sweet May," K 596

Wolfgang Amadeus Mozart
(1756 – 1791)

Allegro Finale

Joseph Haydn
(1732–1809)

Sixth Leçon

Daniel Steibelt
(1765–1823)

Allegretto

Entrée

Andante

Ignaz Pleyel
(1757–1831)

La Marmotte

"A Merry Song" Op. 52, No. 7

Ludwig van Beethoven
(1770 – 1827)

Country Dance

Ludwig van Beethoven
(1770 – 1827)

Fine

D.C. al Fine

Ecossaise

Carl Maria von Weber
(1786–1826)

Two Ländler

1.

Franz Schubert
(1797–1828)

Commodo; ben ritmo

2.

Romance

from Sonatina in G

Ludwig van Beethoven
(1770–1827)

Tyrolienne

Carl Czerny
(1791–1850)

Allegretto

Fine

dim. e poco rall.

D.C.

Two Ecossaises

1.

Friedrich Kuhlau
(1786 – 1832)

2.

The Hiding Cuckoo

from the sketch book for "Album For The Young"

Robert Schumann
(1810-1856)

Blindman's Buff

from the sketch book for "Album For The Young"

Robert Schumann
(1810-1856)

Allegro giocoso

Melody
from "Album For The Young"

Robert Schumann
(1810–1856)

Moderato

At A Venetian Lagune

from the sketch book for "Album For The Young"

Robert Schumann
(1810–1856)

Mazurka

Frederic Chopin
(1810 – 1849)

Waltz

Frederic Chopin
(1810 –1849)

Con moto rubato

Polka

Mikhail Ivanovich Glinka
(1804-1857)

Intermezzo

Mikhail Ivanovich Glinka
（1804 – 1857）

D.C. al Fine

Song Without Words

Op. 102, No. 6

Felix Mendelssohn-Bartholdy
(1809-1847)

* Octaves in the original

The Little Soldiers

Allegretto marziale

Stephen Heller
(1813 - 1888)

*Original in 2/4

The Doll's Funeral March

Peter Ilyich Tchaikovsky
(1840–1893)

Dance Of The Gnomes

Ede Poldini
(1869–1957)

Waltz

Johannes Brahms
(1833–1897)

*Original key G#

Album Leaf

Franz Liszt
(1811 – 1886)

Grandfather's Musical Clock

Wilhelm Rohde
(1856–1928)

Con moto

Little Scherzo

Karl Heinrich Reinecke
(1824–1910)

Allegretto

Night Song

Robert Volkmann
(1815 - 1833)

Andantino

Printed and bound in Great Britain by
Caligraving Limited Thetford Norfolk

1/97 (26823)